LEARNING TO LIVE SERIES

YOUR PART IN HIS PLAN

NAVPRESS

A MINISTRY OF THE NAVIGATORS
P.O. Box 6000, Colorado Springs, Colorado 80934

The Navigators is an international Christian organization. Jesus Christ gave His followers the Great Commission to go and make disciples (Matthew 28:19). The aim of The Navigators is to help fulfill that commission by multiplying laborers for Christ in every nation.

NavPress is the publishing ministry of The Navigators. NavPress publications are tools to help Christians grow. Although publications alone cannot make disciples or change lives, they can help believers learn biblical discipleship, and apply what they learn to their lives and ministries.

© 1987 The Navigators Great Britain
All rights reserved, including translation
ISBN: 0-89109-060-6
10603

Printed in the United States of America

Contents

Author

The LEARNING TO LIVE series was written by Peter Dowse. Born in Great Britain, he has degrees from Cambridge University and London Bible College. Peter has been on staff with The Navigators since 1977. He led the student ministry at Sheffield University for several years, and now gives his time to writing and speaking.

Make the Most of This Bible Study

We live in a world of shifting values and conflicting viewpoints. Is it possible in the midst of this to know what is right and what is true? Yes it is! For God is true, and He has chosen to give us in the Bible a definitive expression of His own mind and will, His knowledge of reality, and His thoughts and plans for the world.

> *You will know the truth,*
> *and the truth will set you free.*
> (JOHN 8:32)

It is the aim of this Bible study series to introduce you to the joy and privilege of digging out that truth for yourself.

Personal Bible study is demanding. You will need to give it much time and serious endeavor. In this series, each lesson takes two to three hours to prepare. The rewards of personal Bible study, however, are great. You will surely discover this for yourself as you complete the books in this series.

Remember that Bible study is not merely an academic exercise. You will need to think, but don't forget that the Bible is God's Word. Pray before you start each lesson. Ask God to help you understand the truths and make you sensitive to what He wants to say to you through a particular lesson. Pray as you study, "Lord, what does this mean? How does this relate to me?" Praise Him when you discover something that excites you. The fruit of Bible study should not be just increased head knowledge; it should produce a deeper relationship with God and a lifestyle that is more honoring to Him.

If you can find others who are willing to put in the time to do personal preparation, you will find great value in meeting together to discuss each lesson. But don't let the absence of such a group deter you. Get into God's Word for yourself. You won't be disappointed.

> *When your words came, I ate them;*
> *they were my joy and my heart's delight.*
> (JEREMIAH 15:16)

SOME EXPLANATIONS: The definitions given throughout this series are, of necessity, brief. More exhaustive definitions of the words can be found in any good Bible dictionary, for example, *The Illustrated Bible Dictionary*, published by Inter-Varsity Press.

Whenever the name of a person who has been quoted is followed by an asterisk, you will find information about that person in "Who's Who" on page 103.

Each lesson has sections entitled "Ask Yourself." These do not require written responses, though you may want to write answers to the questions in a notebook. Each lesson also has a section entitled "For Further Study." These sections are optional.

The six books in the *Learning to Live* series can be done in any order, or you can follow this suggested sequence:

Clarifying Your Commitment
Living by His Grace
Living in the World
Disciplines of Living
Your Part in His Plan
Standing Firm

Doing Your Part

In this book, we will consider some of God's purposes for this world, and the implications for Christian service. While God wants worshipers first, and workers second, there can be no doubt that there is work to be done. As we draw closer to God, we inevitably identify with His concerns. This, in turn, motivates us to want to do our part in seeing God's purposes fulfilled.

We can be involved in a *great* work! There is no room for complacency; there is no excuse for boredom. It is also a challenging work. Service involves suffering; the Kingdom of God advances only at cost. Because the forces of evil are real and powerful, serving God requires commitment and maturity.

Sadly, the Church of Jesus Christ includes many inactive or ineffective members. As you begin this book, perhaps you could pray this prayer of Bishop Stratford, the seventeenth-century Bishop of Chester: "Lord, let me not live to be useless."

Belonging to the Church of Christ

The New Testament describes the Church in glowing terms: "Christ loved the church and gave himself up for her" (Ephesians 5:25). According to Revelation 19:7-8, the Church is, in fact, Christ's bride-to-be.

More than that, the Church is central in God's plans for the world. Not only is it a sign of what God is going to do in the future; it is also an agent of what He is doing in the present, and gives Christians the opportunity to be involved in God's plans.

Just what is the Church? Our frequent use of the word to describe a building bears little similarity to the New Testament meaning of the word. But what about our use of the word to identify the Roman Catholic Church or a denomination such as Baptist or Presbyterian?

Pause for Prayer

Our understanding of the New Testament can be colored by presuppositions based on the form of church life with which we are familiar. We need to ask God to help us examine the biblical evidence afresh. We need His help to find dynamic principles of life for growth and order. These principles will arm us with new attitudes and new vision for the realities of modern church life.

9

The Nature of the Church

To the church of God in Corinth,
to those sanctified in Christ Jesus and called to be holy,
together with all those everywhere who call on the name
of our Lord Jesus Christ—their Lord and ours.

(1 Corinthians 1:2)

We will give special attention in this section to the Apostle
Paul's letter to the Ephesians. This letter contains much teaching on the nature of the Church, and is well worth reading.

---

1. The Greek word translated "Church" is *ekklesia*. It is derived
   from *ek*—"out of," and *klesis*—"calling." The Church consists of people who have been called out. According to the
   following references in Ephesians, how are people called out
   (to become part of the Church)?

   1:3-8

   He predestined us to be adopted
   as His sons through Jesus Christ.
   In Him we have redemption through
   His blood

   1:11-14

   We were predestined, having believed
   in Jesus Christ, we are sealed with
   the Holy Spirit, guaranteeing our inheritance

   2:1-10

   For it is by Grace you have been saved,
   through faith, and this not from your-
   selves, it is a gift of God-not by works
   so that no one can boast.

10

"Yes! I am a Christian! How did you know?"

2. The word *ekklesia* is also used in the Greek version of the Old Testament to describe the people of God called together. Read Ephesians 2:11-3:6.

   a. According to this passage, and 1 Peter 2:9-10, how did God bring the Church together as His people?

allowed the Gentiles to come in

   b. What can you learn from the description of God's people as a temple? Also look at 1 Peter 2:4-5.

are being built into a spiritual house

"The church is never a place, but always a people; never a fold but always a flock; never a sacred building but always a believing assembly. The church is you who pray, not where you pray. A structure of brick or marble can no more be a church than your clothes of serge or satin can be you. There is in this world nothing sacred but man, no sanctuary of man but the soul."[1]

—JOHN HAVLIK

---

3. Look at the following references in Ephesians. What do they reveal about the place of the Church in God's plans?

1:9-10

to bring all things in heaven and on heart together under one Head, even Christ

12

3:10-11 *To let the rulers and authorities in the heavenly realms, know through the church, Gods wisdom*

3:20-21 *That God be glorified through the church and Jesus Christ*

---

4. The focus of Ephesians is on the *one* Church, which consists of the worldwide, everlasting company of God's people. However, at any particular moment, this Church becomes visible to the world as local gatherings of Christians. In fact, this is the meaning of *ekklesia* in the vast majority of New Testament references, and matches the most common usage of the word in the Greek-speaking world, which was to denote a public gathering of citizens. (For an example, see Acts 19:39 [NIV] where *ekklesia* is translated as "assembly.")

How did this development of local churches take place? Look up the following passages in Acts.

11:19-26 *being scattered by persecution, they went out and preached the good news*

13:1-3 *by worshiping and fasting, the Holy Spirit sent Barnabas and Saul out.*

14:21-23 *They preached the good news, then by strengthening the disciples. They also appointed Elders*

15:36-41 *Because of the disagreement they covered more ground.*

They strengthened the churches

The Book of Acts makes exciting reading as it charts the spread of the gospel and the establishing of numerous churches. Generally speaking, these local gatherings of Christians met in houses. (For examples, see Romans 16:2-5 and Colossians 4:15.) In a city the size of Ephesus, there may well have been several house churches.

---

5. Read Ephesians 4:1-6.

    a. What is the basis for the unity of the worldwide Church?

    One Lord, one faith, one baptism, one God and Father of all.

    b. How should this reflect itself in relationships between local churches?

    we are one body

ASK YOURSELF: **a.** If the Church is people, what implications does this have for my attitude toward church buildings and denominations? **b.** What attitudes do I need to change if I am to do my part in expressing and preserving the unity of the Church?

Jesus and the Church

I will build my church.

(Matthew 16:18)

It is sometimes said that Jesus did not foresee the development of the Church. But two passages in Matthew clearly demonstrate that this is not the case. In both of them, Jesus speaks of the Church in precisely the same terms we have just used—the worldwide, everlasting company of God's people and the local gathering of believers.

---

6. The first passage is Matthew 16:13-20.

   a. Why is it significant that Jesus speaks about the Church at this time in His earthly ministry?

   Because God inspired Peter that Jesus is the Son of the living God, and that He would build the church around Peter

   b. How does this passage encourage you concerning the worldwide Church?

   because the gates of Hades will not overcome it

   (For a full discussion of the possible meanings of verse 19, consult a good Bible commentary. Peter's role in the early Christian mission was a very significant one. However, passages like Acts 15 and Galatians 1 and 2 indicate that he was not in authority over the other apostles.)

15

7. The second passage is Matthew 18:15-20.

   a. What can you learn about the local church?

   that the church, the body will have authority?

   b. How are you encouraged about the local church?

   because Jesus wanted us to have a church.

"Where three are gathered together, there is a church, even though they be laymen." — TERTULLIAN*

ASK YOURSELF: How should Jesus' teaching about the Church affect my attitude toward it?

An Example of Church Life
All the believers were together.
(Acts 2:44)

We have little indication of what took place when churches met. At Corinth there were problems in the churches. The letter Paul wrote to deal with the problems gives some insight into the practices there. (See 1 Corinthians 11:17-34 and 14:26-33.) In all probability, different churches operated in different ways.

8. Acts 2:42-47 describes the first church in Jerusalem. Read these verses two or three times.

a. What activities were central in their gatherings?

teaching, breaking of bread, prayer praising God

Note: Lesson 6 in the book entitled *Living by His Grace* is a more detailed study of the nature of true biblical fellowship.

b. What attitudes did the people have?

glad and sincere hearts, enjoying the favor of all the people

"Church history reveals a recurrent tendency to absolutize and institutionalize the large-group, wedding it to a specific building and form, while at the same time neglecting or even condemning the small group. Virtually every major movement of spiritual renewal in the Christian Church has been accompanied by a return to the small group and the proliferation of such groups of some kind in private homes for Bible study, prayer, and the discussion of the faith."[2] — HOWARD SNYDER

9. Focus on Acts 2:47. What impact did the Church make on people?

They enjoyed church activities,

The church, the people is where they came to hear the gospel and were saved

17

For Further Study

One feature of church life that emerges in Acts 5 is discipline of members who sin (verses 1-11). What can you learn from the following passages about the need for a church to take responsible action when a member persists in sin?

Matthew 18:15-17

1 Corinthians 5:1-13

2 Thessalonians 3:6-16

ASK YOURSELF: How does my involvement with other believers compare with that described in Acts?

A Pattern for Church Growth

From him [Christ] the whole body,
joined and held together by every supporting ligament,
grows and builds itself up in love,
as each part does its work.
(Ephesians 4:16)

For this final section, read Ephesians 4:7-16.

---

10. Concentrate on verses 7 and 8.

 a. What has been given to every Christian? Also read
 1 Peter 4:10.

 Grace (Gifts)

 b. What is the result of this, according to Romans 12:4-6?

 different Gifts to help others

 There are several lists of gifts in the New Testament
(Romans 12:6-8, 1 Corinthians 12:8-10, 1 Corinthians
12:28-30, Ephesians 4:11, and 1 Peter 4:10-11). The lack of
consistency in these lists suggests that they are illustra-
tive rather than exhaustive.
 The point is this: While every Christian is involved in
the Church's mission in a general way through personal
witness to Christ in the world, every Christian also has a
specific gift that enables him to fulfill a specific role
within that mission. Some gifts are more "inward" in
teaching and caring for Christians. Other gifts are "outward" to the world in service or evangelism.

11. Read Ephesians 4:11-12.

   a. What did God give to the Church?

   gifts

   b. What is the specific purpose of God's gift?

   to prepare Gods people for works of service so that the body of Christ may be built up

---

"The task of the ordained ministry is not simply to minister to the congregation but to create and direct a ministering congregation through the detection, development and deployment of God-given resources. . . . The mission which Christ has committed to his Church represents the greatest enterprize with which we can be identified. Its implementation requires the total mobilization of all our God-given resources in unending waves of committed creativity."[3] — EDDIE GIBBS

---

12. How is God's intention for the Church described in Ephesians 4:13-16?

   to reach unity in Jesus, and to become mature Christians,

13. Read Acts 14:23.

   a. What provision was made for the leadership of the local churches? (Do not equate local leaders with the leaders of the Church at large, referred to in Ephesians 4:11.)

   they appointed elders

   b. What significance do you see in the fact that there were several leaders in each church?

   so not one person would rule, more than one leader is a safe guard against satans attacks

   c. According to Hebrews 13:17, what should our attitude be toward those in leadership in the church?

   to obey and submit to their authority

For Further Study
The qualifications for church leaders are listed in 1 Timothy 3:1-13 and Titus 1:6-9. What can you learn from these passages?

to obey an

The following diagram, taken from "The Church as God's Agent in Evangelism," by Howard Snyder, provides a useful illustration of the pattern for church growth.[4]

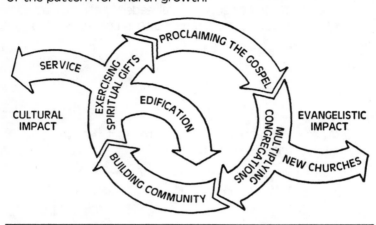

ASK YOURSELF: How can I best develop and use my gifts as a member of Christ's Church?

Stop, Think, and Pray

How has your understanding of the nature of the Church deepened? Has God showed you how you can play a more effective part in the Church? Record below what you think God is speaking to you about, and prayerfully consider what your response should be.

One way to remember the truths you have studied is to choose key Bible verses and memorize them. You can select your own verses from the passages you study, or memorize the one suggested at the end of each lesson. (See page 101 for help in memorizing Scripture.)

Suggested memory verses about belonging to the Church of Christ

As you come to him, the living Stone—rejected by men but chosen by God and precious to him—you also, like living stones, are being built into a spiritual house to be a holy priesthood, offering spiritual sacrifices acceptable to God through Jesus Christ. (1 Peter 2:4-5)

NOTES: 1. John Havlik, *People-Centered Evangelism* (Nashville, Tennessee: Broadman Press, 1971), page 47.

2. Howard Snyder, "The Church as God's Agent in Evangelism," *International Congress on World Evangelization* (Lausanne, Switzerland, 1974), pages 6-7.

3. Eddie Gibbs, *I Believe in Church Growth* (Grand Rapids, Michigan: Eerdmans Publishing Company, 1982), pages 254-255.

4. Snyder, "The Church as God's Agent in Evangelism," *Let the Earth Hear His Voice* (Minneapolis, Minnesota: World Wide Publications, 1975), page 335.

Being Witnesses for Christ

Having completed the work of saving humanity, Jesus returned to His Father in Heaven. But how would the message of what He had done be made known? Incredible though it seems, Jesus committed that task to His disciples. They were to be witnesses to who He was and what He had done. Such was the success of their witness that within a few years, their opponents charged that they had "turned the world upside down" (Acts 17:6, RSV).

The task goes on. Christ has His witnesses today. Who are they? What does it take to be an effective witness? In this lesson we will examine Jesus' teaching, and take a look at the example of the Apostle Paul.

Pause for Prayer

Take a moment to think about those people who in one way or another were witnesses for Christ in your life. Thank God for them and for your salvation in Christ. Then pray that this lesson will help others find salvation through your witness.

Workers and Witnesses

You will be my witnesses.

(Acts 1:8)

25

1. Read Jesus' statement in Matthew 9:35-38.

   a. How did He view the people around Him?

   b. What did He identify as the key to reaching them?

   c. Read Matthew 10:1-8 to see how He reacted to the
   needs of the people.

2. Jesus also spoke about the harvest of people in John
   4:35-38.

   a. What does this passage bring out about the phases of
   evangelism?

   b. Which phase of evangelism is described as "the hard
   work"?

c. What could prevent a harvest?

---

3. After Jesus rose from the dead, He gave His disciples a plan for the future, commonly referred to as the Great Commission. Each gospel refers to it. Read the versions given in Luke 24:45-49 and Acts 1:6-8.

   a. What did Jesus expect of His disciples?

   b. What did He promise them?

WITNESS: primarily a legal term. It was used in Greek for a person attesting to facts and events or asserting the truth. The personal involvement and assurance of the witness was an important element. The disciples were witnesses to the fact that Jesus rose from the dead.

In more general terms, witnessing *(martureo)* means making known the good news of Jesus Christ. Other common New Testament words with essentially the same meaning are preaching *(kerusso)* and evangelism *(euangelizo)*.

---

4. In Matthew 28:18-20 we read that the apostles were told to pass on the Great Commission to other believers. How did other believers respond to the task of witnessing for Christ?

Acts 8:1,4

Acts 11:19-21

It is clear in the New Testament that while some are gifted to be evangelists, all believers are to engage in evangelism. The same applies to functions like serving, giving, and encouraging, which are all spoken of as gifts in Romans 12:6-8. The person with a specific gift sets an example in that area for others to follow.

"I cannot believe in the salvation of anyone who does not work for his neighbor's salvation." —JOHN CHRYSOSTOM*

ASK YOURSELF: What have I learned about the task of witnessing?

Motivated Messengers

We try to persuade men.
(2 Corinthians 5:11)

In his second letter to the church at Corinth, the Apostle Paul bares his heart. He tells of the difficulties of ministry and the temptation to lose heart. But he also reveals his eagerness to communicate the message of Christ. Read 2 Corinthians 5:10-21 several times, and then answer questions 5-7.

---

5. What factors motivated Paul and his fellow missionaries to keep going in evangelism?

"Let's face it: evangelism is not an easy task. There are many discouragements and disappointments."[1] — DAVID WATSON

---

6. What was the essence of Paul's gospel message?

---

7. What did he see as his role in helping people come to God?

30

"The ambassador, before acting, receives a commission from the power for whom he acts. The ambassador, while acting, acts not only as an agent, but as a representative of his sovereign. Lastly, the ambassador's duty is not merely to deliver a definite message, to carry out a definite policy; but he is obliged to watch for opportunities, to study characters, to cast about for expedients, so that he may place it before his hearers in its most attractive form. He is a diplomatist." —JOSEPH B. LIGHTFOOT*

ASK YOURSELF: What can I learn about witnessing from Paul's example?

Into the World

I have sent them into the world.
(John 17:18)

In John 17, shortly before His death, Jesus prays for His disciples. In His prayer, we see His plan for reaching others. Read verses 13-23 several times. (The word *world* refers to organized society that excludes God.)

---

8. Focus on verses 15 and 18.

   a. How does Jesus want His disciples to relate to the world?

b. Jesus exemplified this principle; in derision, He was called "a friend of sinners" (Matthew 11:19). What can you learn from Mark 2:15-17 about the behavior that earned Him this title?

c. According to 1 Corinthians 9:19-23, what is involved in relating to those who are not Christians? Include practical illustrations for today.

d. According to John 17:14, what response can we expect on occasion? How might this be expressed today?

"Some like to live within the sound of church or chapel bell; I'd rather run a rescue shop within a yard of hell."—WILLIAM BOOTH*

9. Read John 17:16 and 17.

   a. How did Jesus expect His disciples to be different?

   b. According to Matthew 5:16 and 6:1, what does this involve?

"The sermons most needed today are sermons in shoes."

— C.H. SPURGEON*

10. Continue reading in John 17, verses 21-23.

   a. How do relationships between Christians affect nonbelievers?

b. According to John 13:34-35, what is the key to this?

c. What other reason can you find in Romans 12:4-6 for working together in evangelism?

ASK YOURSELF: In what ways can I give my nonChristian friends the opportunity to become acquainted with my Christian friends?

---

11. Consider John 17:20.

a. Also read Romans 10:17. What is essential if sinners are to come to believe in Christ?

b. As we preach the message, the Holy Spirit is at work. How does He work, according to John 16:8-11?

c. Read Acts 13:42-44 and 17:32. What effect can the gospel message have even on those who are not yet ready to believe in Christ?

d. What should every Christian be ready to do? See Colossians 4:5-6 and 1 Peter 3:15.

ASK YOURSELF: Can I clearly explain the Christian message? Which of my Christian friends would listen to me, and then suggest improvements?

---

12. It is clear from John 17:20 that Jesus expects others to believe in Him.

a. What promises had He made to His disciples in John 15:1-17?

The word *fruit* here has a double meaning. In the first place, it refers to a quality of life, described in Galatians 5:22-23. Such a life will influence others for Christ, yielding the fruit of new Christians.

b. If these promises are to be fulfilled, what attitude do we need to have?

"Count on God's good faith. Do not grieve and dishonor Him through disbelieving Him. . . . Prayer is God's mightiest instrument in the salvation of souls, and it is to be doubted if any soul is saved apart from the believing prayer of some saint."[2]

—J. OSWALD SANDERS

ASK YOURSELF: Am I prayerfully expecting God to use my witness and bring others to faith?

For Further Study

Study the example of Jesus in John 4. What can you learn from the way He witnessed to the Samaritan woman?

Stop, Think, and Pray

Look back over the "Ask Yourself" questions. What is God teaching you about being a witness? What practical steps should you take in order to be a more effective witness for Christ?

NOTES: 1. David Watson, *I Believe in Evangelism* (Grand Rapids, Michigan: Eerdmans Publishing Co., 1976), page 83.
2. J. Oswald Sanders, *The Divine Art of Soulwinning* (Chicago: Moody Press, n.d.), pages 42-43.

Strengthening New Believers in Christ

There's a celebration in Heaven when someone repents of his sin and turns to Christ (Luke 15:10). There should be a celebration on earth too! Someone has been forgiven and adopted into God's family; he has become a part of God's new creation; he is destined to spend eternity with Him.

These are all good reasons for celebrating! In addition, a new believer now has the potential to grow and develop into a mature disciple of Christ, someone whose life brings glory to God and influences others to come to know Him.

Unfortunately, for many this potential is never realized. They remain spiritual babies, immature in their faith and ineffective in their service. A prime reason is that they are often neglected after becoming Christians. They are left to fend for themselves. This is far from God's intention. His desire is that each one should be strengthened and brought to maturity. What does the Bible teach about this, and how can it be accomplished?

Pause for Prayer

Thank God for the people who have helped you grow as a Christian. Then ask God to use this lesson to teach you about the ministry of strengthening other Christians, and to show you what part you can have in it.

The Commission to Care

I will give you shepherds after my own heart.
(Jeremiah 3:15)

1. What can you learn from Jesus' instructions to Simon Peter in the following references?

Luke 22:31-32

John 21:15-17

2. In the previous lesson we looked at the Great Commission as it relates to evangelism. What does Matthew 28:18-20 teach about the care of new believers? (The first disciples had, of course, experienced this care from Jesus Himself. In all that they did, they must have constantly been reminded of how Jesus had helped them grow. He was their model.)

"This is the great work: not only to bring souls to believe in Christ, but to build them up in our most holy faith. How grievously are they mistaken who imagine that as soon as children are born, they need take no more care of them! We do not find it so. The chief care then begins." —JOHN WESLEY*

The Apostles in Action

*I have not hesitated to proclaim to you
the whole will of God.*
(Acts 20:27)

---

3. What can you learn from the following references about how the apostles obeyed Jesus' commission and cared for new Christians?

   Acts 2:40-42 (Many of these converts had expected to stay in Jerusalem only for a few days. Acts 2:44-45 may describe emergency measures taken to enable them to stay longer.)

   Acts 5:40-42

   Acts 11:19-26

---

4. What did the Apostle Paul do about the follow-up of new believers?

41

Acts 14:21-23 (For a striking illustration of Paul's commitment to this ministry, look at the treatment he had previously received in these three cities—Acts 13:50-51, 14:5-7, and 14:19-20.)

Acts 15:36-41

Acts 18:23

STRENGTHEN: The word *strengthen* used in Acts 14:22, 15:41, and 18:23 (NIV) is a translation of the Greek word *episterizo*. This is a stronger form of the word *sterizo*, meaning to fix, make fast, or set. The thirteen occurrences of sterizō in the New Testament give insight into the aim and form of a follow-up ministry. The aim of follow-up is discipleship. (The other references are Luke 9:51, 16:26, and 22:32, Romans 1:11 and 16:25, 1 Thessalonians 3:2 and 13, 2 Thessalonians 2:17 and 3:3, James 5:8, 1 Peter 5:10, 2 Peter 1:12, and Revelation 3:2.)

A Ministry for All
Teach and admonish one another.
(Colossians 3:16)

---

5. In the preceding section, we studied the ministry of the apostles. However, as we saw in our study of the Church (lesson 1), God expects every Christian to have a ministry.

42

What indication do the following verses give that every one of us should be involved in strengthening our fellow Christians?

1 Thessalonians 5:11

Hebrews 3:12-13

Hebrews 10:24-25

The truths in these references are of a general nature. They remind us that no Christian is beyond the need for the teaching, the encouragement, and sometimes the rebuke of fellow Christians.

What is true for all of us, is true in a special way for new Christians. As well as general fellowship with others, they need concentrated individual attention. They need strengthening in their new faith until they are healthily independent in their relationship with God.

If this is to happen, *someone* needs to take the initiative. New Christians can find the general encouragement of fellowship, and the examples and teaching of leaders. But the heart of a follow-up ministry is one person working with another as a spiritual parent. It is the lack of individuals willing to take this initiative that leaves so many new Christians weak and immature.

6. What qualities are needed in order to have an effective follow-up ministry?

Romans 15:14

Galatians 6:1

Colossians 3:16

7. How can we become effective in ministry, according to Ephesians 4:11-12?

ASK YOURSELF: a. What have I learned about the ministry of strengthening new Christians? b. What things could prevent me from doing my part in this ministry?

Building with Purpose
But each one should be careful how he builds.
(1 Corinthians 3:10)

8. Consider Colossians 1:28-29.

   a. What was Paul's aim in ministry?

   b. What was he doing to further that aim?

   c. What kind of effort did it involve?

9. Read Colossians 2:1-3 and 4:12-13. What further insight do these passages give into the ministry of bringing others to maturity?

"Prayer is an absolute essential because effective follow-up is really the work of God and his Spirit, and the true goal of follow-up is the formation of Christ in a person's life. You are *his* instrument to help accomplish *his* purposes in the life of *his* child."[1] — WALDRON SCOTT

10. Read 1 Corinthians 3:5-15, a passage that describes the ministry of building Christian maturity into the lives of others. Write down what you consider to be two important principles for such a ministry.

ASK YOURSELF: What steps can I take to have a more purposeful ministry?

Sharing Our Lives

We were delighted to share with you
not only the gospel of God
but our lives as well.
(1 Thessalonians 2:8)

First Thessalonians gives a most helpful account of the way Paul and his team went about their ministry. Chapter 1 describes how they brought the gospel to Thessalonica. The genuine responses of many people there opened the way for an effective follow-up ministry. In chapter 2, verses 1-6, Paul briefly answers those who have criticized his motives, before going on to describe his ministry. Read 1 Thessalonians 2:7-3:13.

11. Focus on 1 Thessalonians 2:7-13. What can you learn about the way Paul and his team strengthened the Thessalonians in their new life?

12. Focus on 1 Thessalonians 2:17-3:10 and read the explanatory notes below. What can you discover here about Paul's attitude toward the Thessalonians?

"torn away" (2:17)—a very strong word; literally, "made an orphan by separation."

"strengthen" (3:2)—a translation of the Greek word *sterizo*; see note on page 42.

"supply what is lacking" (3:10)—also translated as "prepare" or "equip" in Ephesians 4:12. Paul wants to bring his special gifts to bear in equipping the Thessalonians for service.

13. What perspective does 1 Thessalonians 3:11-13 give on the ministry of follow-up?

"No system or program will automatically meet and cure the needs of human beings. Because we are individuals, we each have specific needs which people alone can meet. . . . True growth takes time and tears and love and patience."[2] — LEROY EIMS

Teach: People need to know what the Bible says and means.
Train: People need loving help to translate truth into action.
Transmit: People need the example of another who is following Christ.
Trust: People have their own relationship with God. Ultimately He is the One who will change them.

Practical Exercise (optional)

Defining Our Aim

We have seen Paul's long-term aim for every Christian. Reading in Colossians 2, we see that he also had more immediate goals. In particular, he wanted new Christians to become thoroughly established in their relationship with Christ, learning how to draw on the various resources God has provided for growth.

Mature Christians play an important part in encouraging this growth. To be effective in this ministry, we need to have a clear grasp of where we are going. One way to do this is to list some characteristics that should be established in a Christian during the early months of his new life. A sample list is given below.

- Assured of his salvation and sonship, based on the Bible and the inner witness of the Spirit.
- Committed to growing as a Christian, this being particularly evident in his faith, obedience, and fellowship with God.
- Seeking to know and understand the Bible through teaching, reading, study, and memorization.
- Regularly involved with other Christians in corporate worship and fellowship.
- Identifying with Christ in his environment.

Playing Our Part

Having defined a general aim, we need to think about what we should be working on with the person we are seeking to help.

It is not possible to specify a general plan of action. Every person is unique, so every plan must be unique.

Let us suppose that a person's greatest need lies in the area of fellowship with God. In particular, we want to help him become established in a daily time of reading the Bible and praying. Below is an example of a follow-up plan for a new Christian.

Topic: Fellowship with God

Objective: To begin to spend regular and meaningful time with God by reading the Bible and praying.

Activities
1. Pray regularly that he will *desire* to spend time with God.
2. Show him the example of Jesus spending time with God.
3. Explain a simple plan for having a "quiet time" and do it together, keeping it brief.
4. Continue having quiet times together for a few days, focusing on passages that will strengthen the person's assurance of salvation.
5. Introduce him to a simple plan for reading the Bible. Begin with one of the gospels.
6. Occasionally, have a quiet time together, and discuss things he is discovering in his reading.
7. Look together at verses that show the value of fellowship with God.
8. Give him a helpful booklet or tape on the quiet time.
9. When he is ready, help him develop different patterns for his quiet time, to have some variety.

Scriptures
Mark 1:35—the example of Jesus
Psalm 5:3, Daniel 6:10—the example of others
Matthew 26:41—the importance of prayer in preparing for temptation
Psalm 143:8—a sample prayer for a quiet time

Tools
Booklets: *Seven Minutes with God,* by Robert Foster (NavPress)
    Appointment with God (NavPress)

Tapes: "The Quiet Time," by Stephen Oxford
Bible studies: the *Experiencing God Series,* by Warren and
            Ruth Myers (NavPress)
Books: *Knowing God,* by J.I. Packer (InterVarsity Press)
        Personal Growth materials (NavPress)

This example of a follow-up plan uses the easily memorized acronym TOAST (**T**opic, **O**bjective, **A**ctivities, **S**criptures, **T**ools). Once you have come up with a plan like this, keep it filed somewhere. It may be a helpful resource when you want to help someone else in the future.

Producing plans like this is hard work! Some topics are particularly difficult. We need to pray that God will give us good ideas that are appropriate for the person in mind. Then we need to seek God's wisdom as to when to do the various things we have planned. It can be tempting to "dump" everything we know on the person in one or two heavy sessions. However, wise follow-up moves step by step, at a pace appropriate for the person.

Now that you have seen this example, look again at the list of aims on page 48. Choose another topic and develop a follow-up plan. Write the plan on a separate piece of paper because you will probably want to keep it for future reference.

Stop, Think, and Pray

What have you learned about the ministry of strengthening new believers? How can you begin to apply what you have learned? What do you need to do to become better prepared to help someone? Do you need to pray earnestly that God will give you someone you can help in this way? Write down your response to God's Word.

Suggested memory verses about strengthening new believers in Christ

As apostles of Christ we could have been a burden to you, but we were gentle among you, like a mother caring for her little children. We loved you so much that we were delighted to share with you not only the gospel of God but our lives as well, because you had become so dear to us.
(1 Thessalonians 2:7-8)

NOTES: 1. Waldron Scott, "Being a Spiritual Parent," *Discipleship Journal,* vol. 1, no. 1, January/February 1981, page 38.
2. LeRoy Eims, *The Lost Art of Disciplemaking* (Grand Rapids, Michigan: Zondervan Publishing House, 1978), pages 50 and 12.

Evangelizing the World for Christ

We have focused on the task Jesus Christ committed to His disciples, that of being His witnesses. We have seen that this task involves not only preaching the gospel, but also teaching and encouraging the new believers. It is easy to become pre-occupied with our own sphere of influence; we forget that our neighborhood, or our town, or even our country, is not all there is. A world of over 4 billion people is waiting to be reached for Jesus Christ. God wants us to have the privilege of *both* reaching out to our next-door neighbor with the gospel of Christ *and* contributing to the great task of world evangeli-zation. If we are to do both, we will need vision.

Pause for Prayer
Be quiet for a moment before you begin. Ask God to work through this lesson to make your heart more like His own.

God's Concern for the World
God so loved the world.
(John 3:16)

Read carefully 1 Timothy 2:1-7. This passage, especially verses 3-7, provides the focus for our study in this first section. We will also consider a number of cross-references.

1. Read verses 3 and 4.

   a. What is the extent of God's love?

   b. John 3:16-18 is printed below. Underline key words or phrases that reveal the extent of God's love.

   > *For God so loved the world that he gave his one and only Son, that whoever believes in him shall not perish but have eternal life. For God did not send his Son into the world to condemn the world, but to save the world through him. Whoever believes in him is not condemned, but whoever does not believe stands condemned already because he has not believed in the name of God's one and only Son.*

   c. Read Jesus' parables in Luke 15:3-10. What do they reveal about God's love?

2. Read verse 5 of 1 Timothy 2.

   a. What does Paul (the writer) say about Jesus Christ?

b. How does this compare with Jesus' own statements in John 8:12 and 14:6?

To say that there is no way of salvation other than Jesus Christ is not to say that there is *no* truth in other religions. Clearly there is. However, at best it is partial truth, and in many cases it is mixed with serious error. It is important in witnessing to those of other faiths that we find areas of truth with which we can identify.

3. Consider 1 Timothy 2:6-7.

a. What is the scope of Christ's work?

b. How is this reinforced in John 1:29 and 4:42?

Additional reference: 1 John 2:1-2

c. How did Paul link together the breadth of Christ's work and his own ministry?

"The most categorical affirmation of God's will to save the world is made in the person and work of his Son Jesus Christ. Our difficulties in explaining how it is possible that, in spite of the fact that God's will is that his salvation reach all men (1 Timothy 2:4), not all are actually saved, should not lead us to deny the universal scope."[1] — RENÉ PADILLA

Our Concern for the World
The field is the world.
(Matthew 13:38)

4. Read the various statements of Jesus' Great Commission recorded in the passages below. For each reference, write down key words that express the scope of the task.

   Matthew 28:18-20

   Mark 16:15-16

   Luke 24:46-48

John 17:18, 20:21

---

5. What challenge and promise are found in Matthew 24:14?

---

6. Read Matthew 9:35-38.

   a. In light of the truths we have examined in this lesson, how would you define the "harvest field"?

   b. What implication does this have for your praying?

"World vision is getting on your heart what is on God's heart—the world." — DAWSON TROTMAN*

ASK YOURSELF: How can I strengthen my commitment to world missions?

Crossing Cultures for Christ

You will be my witnesses in Jerusalem,
and in all Judea and Samaria,
and to the ends of the earth.
(Acts 1:8)

7. What can you learn from the prophecies recorded in Revelation 5:9-10 and 7:9-10 about the evangelization of the world?

Additional reference: Revelation 21:22-27

We usually think of the world in terms of two hundred or so countries. In reality, mankind is a far more complex mosaic of people with numerous cultural and linguistic differences. (See page 100 for suggestions on developing world vision.) Consider this statement by Ralph Winter, an authority on missions:

Most conversions . . . take place as the result of some Christian witnessing to a near neighbor. The awesome problem is . . . that most non-Christians in the world today are not culturally near neighbors of any Christians, and that it will take a special kind of "cross-cultural" evangelism to reach them.[2]

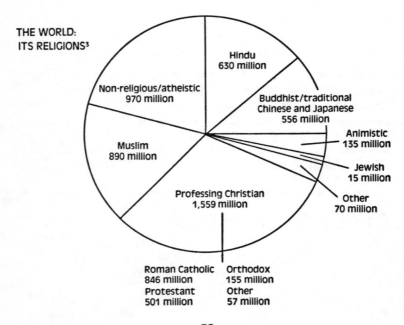

THE WORLD: ITS RELIGIONS[3]

Hindu
630 million

Non-religious/atheistic
970 million

Buddhist/traditional
Chinese and Japanese
556 million

Animistic
135 million

Muslim
890 million

Jewish
15 million

Other
70 million

Professing Christian
1,559 million

Roman Catholic
846 million
Protestant
501 million

Orthodox
155 million
Other
57 million

THE WORLD: ITS PEOPLES[4]

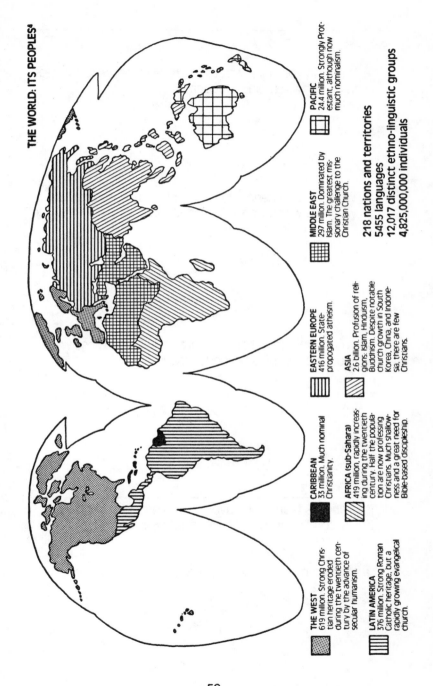

THE WEST
619 million. Strong Christian heritage eroded during the twentieth century by the advance of secular humanism.

LATIN AMERICA
376 million. Strong Roman Catholic heritage, but a rapidly growing evangelical church.

CARIBBEAN
33 million. Much nominal Christianity.

AFRICA (sub-Sahara)
419 million, rapidly increasing during the twentieth century. Half the population are now professing Christians. Much shallowness and a great need for Bible-based discipleship.

EASTERN EUROPE
416 million. State-propagated atheism.

ASIA
2.6 billion. Profusion of religions: Islam, Hinduism, Buddhism. Despite notable church growth in South Korea, China, and Indonesia, there are few Christians.

MIDDLE EAST
297 million. Dominated by Islam. The greatest missionary challenge to the Christian Church.

PACIFIC
24.4 million. Strongly Protestant, although now much nominalism.

**218 nations and territories
5455 languages
12,017 distinct ethno-linguistic groups
4,825,000,000 individuals**

59

8. Prayerfully consider Acts 1:8.

   a. What do you think was the difference between witness-
      ing in Jerusalem and in Judea?

   b. What new challenge do you think confronted someone
      who was witnessing in Samaria? (Read John 4:4-42 to see
      how Jesus did it.)

   c. What additional challenges probably faced those who
      sought to witness beyond Samaria?

9. Paul and his team were involved in cross-cultural evangelism. Second Corinthians 1:3-11 gives insight into that
   experience.

   a. What can you learn about the cost of this kind of
      service?

b. What kind of support did Paul want from the Corinthians?

c. According to 1 Corinthians 9:13-14, what other kind of support do such people deserve?

"The Spirit of Christ is a Spirit of missions, and the nearer we get to him the more intensely missionary we must become."

— HENRY MARTYN*

ASK YOURSELF: a. How can I decide if God wants me to be a cross-cultural missionary? (You may want to ask others for suggestions!) **b.** How can I strengthen my support of those who are involved in such work?

Multiplying Your Life for Christ
The least of you will become a thousand.
(Isaiah 60:22)

---

10. Jesus' concern was for the world. But what was His strategy for reaching that world? Read His prayer in John 17 and then summarize His plan.

11. What illustrations of this strategy do you find in the following references in Mark's gospel?

3:13-19

4:33-34

6:7-13, 30

9:30-31

16:15

"Next to His redeeming work on Calvary, our Lord Jesus gave greatest attention to the twelve whom He appointed 'to be with Him.' We . . . major on understanding Christ's *redeeming* work and neglect, to our great cost, to study His *training* work. They are two parts of one great whole."[5] —J.H. MARTIN

12. Read 2 Timothy 2:2. Then consider it phrase by phrase.

a. How did Paul minister to Timothy before he gave this command? (See Acts 16:1-3 and 2 Timothy 3:10-11.)

b. How did Paul expect Timothy to imitate this kind of ministry?

c. What was Timothy to expect from those to whom he ministered?

We may not be pioneer missionaries like Paul, or have the gifts of Timothy. But we can be faithful people who share what we know with others. In this way, with the help and support of others in our church, we can multiply our impact for Jesus Christ. The potential is enormous.

Think of a new Christian, perhaps someone you led to Christ. Suppose that you help her get established in her new faith and learn how to witness. (You may not be the only influence, but you take a special interest in her growth.) After two years, you both lead another person to Christ and help her grow. In four years there are four committed disciples; in six years, eight; in eight years, sixteen. Forty years later there are over a million committed disciples.

Of course it is not as simple as that. Spiritual forces are at work. There are cultures to be crossed and languages to be learned. In some places, there may be years of sowing before the first fruit comes. Nevertheless, the power of multiplication must be utilized.

The wonderful thing is that you don't have to be a great evangelist to do your part. You simply need to learn how to be a friend to nonChristians and, in time, lead some individuals to Christ. Then you need the vision and commitment to give new Christians the help they need to grow and become fruitful.

Perhaps you will need help first of all, but ultimately you can look forward to a ministry of multiplication for Jesus Christ, and can play a significant part in world evangelization.

---

13. Focus on Isaiah 60:22. This promise was given to Isaiah for the people of Israel. Jesus, however, applied these later chapters of Isaiah to His own ministry.

   a. What kind of person does God use?

   b. What attitude should we have in giving ourselves for the Lord's use?

ASK YOURSELF: **a.** How should the idea of multiplication affect the way I am currently living? **b.** How can I trust God to use my life in a significant way?

For Further Study: *Faith and Ministry*

A. What can you learn from the verses on page 65 about the importance of faith?

Matthew 9:27-31

Matthew 13:58

Matthew 17:14-21

Hebrews 11:6

B. For each of the following verses or passages, list the characteristic linked with unbelief.

Mark 16:14

Luke 24:25

Hebrews 3:7-13

1 John 5:10

C. Thinking about your personal ministry, how do the following verses help your faith?

John 14:12-14

John 15:5,8,16

D. Meditate on the following verses. What can you ask God to do for you?

Mark 11:22-24

1 John 5:14-15

Stop, Think, and Pray

Look over the "Ask Yourself" questions in this lesson. They will probably make you think of several things you *could* do. Prayerfully consider these, and ask God what He wants you to do now. Also write down other things you want to be sure to remember in the future.

Suggested memory verse about evangelizing the world for Christ

But you will receive power when the Holy Spirit comes on you; and you will be my witnesses in Jerusalem, and in all Judea and Samaria, and to the ends of the earth. (Acts 1:8)

NOTES: 1. René Padilla, *Let the Earth Hear His Voice* (Minneapolis, Minnesota: World Wide Publications, 1975), page 118.
2. Ralph Winter, *Let the Earth Hear His Voice*, page 213.
3. Patrick Johnstone, *Operation World* (Waynesboro, Georgia: STL Books, 1981). These statistics are accurate as of June, 1985.
4. Johnstone, *Operation World*, page 30.
5. J.H. Martin, forward to *The Master Trainer*, by P.T. Chandapilla (Bombay, India: Gospel Literature Service, 1974), page v.

Changing Society with Christ

Mankind was created to live in community and find fulfillment in social relationships. Yet sin has turned human society into a vehicle for oppression, violence, and injustice.

It is appalling to realize that one-fifth of the human race lacks the basic necessities for survival, and thousands die of starvation each day. They are victims of the injustice of world economics. Others are politically oppressed, denied their fundamental human rights by totalitarian regimes. Still others suffer discrimination on account of their race or sex. In so-called developed nations, millions are oppressed by loneliness and alienation.

What is the answer for society's overwhelming needs? As Christians, we are committed to taking the gospel to the needy millions. But is there more we should be doing? In this lesson we will take a look at the Bible's teaching, and discover a basis for both a deep involvement in society and a commitment to promoting social change.

Pause for Prayer

It is easy to be moved with compassion in considering a subject like this, but not to be moved to action. Ask God to inform your mind and touch your heart through this lesson, but also ask Him to help you make an appropriate response.

Spoiled Society

He looked for justice, but saw bloodshed;
for righteousness, but heard cries of distress.
(Isaiah 5:7)

---

1. Read the following references in Genesis. What do they teach about the place of social relationships in God's plan for humanity, and the disorder introduced by the Fall?

2:18-25

3:6-7

3:16

4:8-9

6:11-12

2. Read Romans 13:1-7.

   a. What does the passage tell us about God's provision for continued order in society?

   b. What is the *intended* role of those in authority?

   c. As Christian citizens, what is our responsibility?

3. How do the following references illustrate God's concern for what goes on in society?

Deuteronomy 16:18-20

Psalm 82:1-4 (The "gods" of verse 1 are probably national leaders; see verses 6 and 7.)

Isaiah 58:1-14

James 5:1-6

There are also numerous illustrations in Hosea, Amos, Isaiah, and Micah. A good example is Amos 1:2-3:2, which is addressed not only to Israel and Judah, but also to the surrounding nations.

"We affirm that God is both the Creator and the Judge of all men. We therefore should share his concern for justice and reconciliation throughout human society and for the liberation of men from every kind of oppression."[1]

ASK YOURSELF: How well do my concerns for society align with God's concerns?

Your Kingdom Come

Your kingdom come,
your will be done
on earth as it is in heaven.
(Matthew 6:10)

---

4. The Old Testament records a continual disparity between what God wants in society, and what actually happens. But the Old Testament also looks forward to a day when God

72

will establish His rule. How is that day described in the following passages in Isaiah?

2:1-5

9:1-7

11:1-9

65:17-25

This "age to come," which is characterized by the establishment of God's rule, is often called "the Kingdom of God" in the New Testament ("Kingdom of Heaven" in Matthew).

---

5. As you read the references in Isaiah, you probably noticed some things that seemed to refer to Jesus' coming, and other things that are still to be fulfilled. When Jesus came to earth, what did *He* teach about the coming of the Kingdom?

Matthew 4:17

Matthew 6:9-10

Luke 11:14-20

Luke 17:20-21

Luke 21:25-31

Luke 22:14-18

Much of the New Testament underlines Jesus' teaching about the Kingdom of God. On the one hand, by His coming, ministry, and His death and resurrection, Jesus has brought the Kingdom of God into human history. On the other hand, the Kingdom is not fully established. This event awaits the return of Jesus and the final overthrow of all the forces of evil. The tension between what has already taken place and what will take place in the future forms the background for much of our understanding of Christian living, and is very relevant as we reflect on our social responsibility.

6. How does Matthew 13:31-33 describe the growth of the Kingdom?

The Kingdom of God is already active in the world. This is seen in its fullest sense in the Church, where men and women explicitly recognize the lordship of Christ and personally enter the Kingdom. It can also be seen in society: whenever God's will is done and evil is overcome, the Kingdom of God advances. This does not mean that we can take the blindly optimistic view of the humanist who says that society is gradually progressing. Alongside the continuing advance of Christ's work, there is an increasing rage on the part of evil anti-Christian forces. Furthermore, all that is established has a temporary nature about it, awaiting the return of Christ when all things will be judged and transformed.

Yet there is continuity between the present and the future; we look forward to transformation, not total replacement. In some way, all that is good in God's creation, and all that has been good about man's stewardship of it in history, will be taken up in the new creation. In light of this, Christians can take their stand for social righteousness and work for social renewal in the certainty that neither they nor their efforts are meaningless or will be lost. On the contrary, despite appearances, they are aligned with the ultimate purpose and goal of history.

---

7. Meditate on Matthew 6:10.

   a. What do you think is meant by the request, "Your king-
      dom come"?

   b. If you pray this way with integrity, what will it mean for
      the way you live?

For Further Study

Revelation 21 gives a New Testament picture of the completed Kingdom. Read through the chapter several times. What aspects of this present earthly life will be excluded from the future Kingdom? What aspects will be included? What most excites you in the chapter? How can you use it as a basis for both praise and requests?

"Our work now is not building the kingdom of God on earth, but the invasion of this earth by the kingdom that will one day totally transform it."[2] — CHRISTOPHER SUGDEN

ASK YOURSELF: How should an understanding of the value of the Kingdom of God affect my attitude toward society?

Changing Society

He chose to give us birth through the word of truth,
that we might be a kind of firstfruits
of all he created.
(James 1:18)

Prayer and Example

8. Read 1 Timothy 2:1-4.

a. What specific responsibility for society is ours as Christians?

b. Based on these verses and what you have already learned about God's concerns for society, what things could you pray about?

---

9. The Church is intended to be an example of what community life is like when lived under the authority of Christ. It is an example to the world of the coming Kingdom of God.

a. What social issues did the early Church grapple with in its desire to be a faithful example?

Romans 14:13-19

2 Corinthians 8:1-15

James 2:1-9

b. What do you think are some pressing issues today in which the Church needs to set an example?

Influence and Action

Christians are part of society. In Matthew 5:13-16, Jesus talks about the kind of influence they should have. Read the passage two or three times, and then consider the questions that follow.

---

10. Focus on verse 13.

   a. What kind of influence do you think Christ expects us to have on society?

   b. What is essential if we are to have that kind of influence?

"Do you think we're getting a bit political?"

11. Sometimes our stand for Christian values will bring us into conflict with authorities. We are commanded to submit to the government. However, this does not necessarily mean that we are to be passive. What can you learn from the following incidents about submitting to authority?

Acts 5:25-42

Acts 16:16-40

"We shall have to repent in this generation not so much for the evil deeds of the wicked people, but for the appalling silence of the good people." — MARTIN LUTHER KING, JR.*

12. Read Matthew 5:14-16.

a. What point is Christ making about Christians and society?

b. Based on the following verses, what actions are expected of true Christians?

Matthew 25:31-46

James 1:27

Two forms of influencing society are distinguished in the lists that follow.

Social service	Social action
Relieving human need	Removing the causes of human need
Philanthropic activity	Political and economic activity
Seeking to minister to individuals and families	Seeking to transform the structures of society
Works of mercy	The quest for justice

Evangelism and Disciplemaking

13. a. According to Matthew 28:18-20, what is one important way in which we are to point to the Kingdom of God?

b. How will this result in a changed society?

"One must understand discipleship in order to make disciples, and discipleship is not fully biblical apart from a commitment to social justice. . . . To be a disciple is to be committed to the King and his Kingdom of just relationships."[3] — WALDRON SCOTT

ASK YOURSELF: **a.** How can my church be a more accurate example of the Kingdom of God? **b.** In what ways can I take more responsibility for society?

Stop, Think, and Pray
How has God spoken to you about your attitude toward society? What one or two specific things can you do right away? Ask God to show you a meaningful response to what you have learned.

Suggested memory verses about changing society with Christ

Is not this the kind of fasting I have chosen:
to loose the chains of injustice
and untie the cords of the yoke,
to set the oppressed free
and break every yoke?
Is it not to share your food with the hungry
and to provide the poor wanderer with shelter—
when you see the naked, to clothe him,
and not to turn away
from your own flesh and blood?
(Isaiah 58:6-7)

NOTES: 1. *Let the Earth Hear His Voice* (Minneapolis, Minnesota: World Wide Publications, 1975), page 4.
2. Christopher Sugden, *Social Gospel or No Gospel?* (Nottingham, England: Grove Books, 1975 and 1977), page 22.
3. Waldron Scott, *Bring Forth Justice* (Grand Rapids, Michigan: Eerdmans Publishing Company, 1980), page xvi.

Expecting the Return of Christ

In our contemporary world, hope is in short supply. We face massive problems created by our own selfishness and our human inadequacies. Dreamers of previous generations looked forward with hope; the realists of today are in despair.

In the midst of all this, Christianity offers a message of hope. It is not an optimistic escapist dream that ignores the reality of evil; it centers on the Person of Christ. Being confident that by His death and resurrection the forces of evil have been dealt a decisive defeat, Christians look forward to the final victory of God and of goodness. This victory will be heralded by the return to earth of the Lord Jesus Christ. This remarkable truth gives perspective and meaning to life.

Pause for Prayer

Open up your mind and heart to God's Holy Spirit. Ask Him to reveal to you through His Word something of what God has in store for His world and His people.

A Sure Promise

Christ . . . will appear a second time,
not to bear sin, but to bring salvation
to those who are waiting for him.
(Hebrews 9:28)

1. Read John 14:1-3. How does Jesus comfort His disciples?

2. Read the account of Jesus' ascension to Heaven in Acts 1:9-11.

   a. What do you think the disciples' feelings were as He ascended?

   b. What promise was given to them?

3. The theme of Christ's return is very prominent in the teaching of the apostles. Glance through 1 Thessalonians and write down statements about Jesus' return, along with references. (You should be able to find something in each chapter.)

Reference	Main thought

(If you want to compare 1 Thessalonians with other books, glance through 1 Peter.)

"The second coming of Christ is not confined to a few obscure passages, nor does belief in it depend on highly imaginative interpretations of symbolic visions. It lies on the surface of the Bible for all to see. . . . There are more than 250 clear references to the return of the Lord in the New Testament."[1] — BRUCE MILNE

ASK YOURSELF: How prominent in my thinking is this sure promise of Jesus' return?

A Momentous Event

The glorious appearing
of our great God and Savior, Jesus Christ.
(Titus 2:13)

Several times Jesus made reference to a future, glorious return. The books of Matthew (chapter 24), Mark (chapter 13), and Luke (chapter 21) include Jesus' teaching about the end of the age and His return. We will focus on Matthew's version, and try to understand its message with the use of cross-references.

4. Focus on Matthew 24:1-31.

a. What did Jesus say will characterize the period before His return?

b. What other characteristics of "the last days" are given in these cross-references?

1 Timothy 4:1-3

2 Timothy 3:1-5

The phrase *the last days* is clearly used in some places to refer to the entire period between Jesus' first and second comings (for example, Acts 2:17 and Hebrews 1:2). In Matthew 24, Jesus lists characteristics of the period between His resurrection and His coming again. These characteristics, or signs, reflect the conflict between good and evil, between God and Satan. As the end approaches, we can expect the conflict to escalate. This should cause increased expectancy among believers, though the actual time of the end cannot be predicted.

c. Why do you think Jesus talked about these signs?

The disciples asked two questions in verse 3: When will the Temple be destroyed? When will You return and bring the age to an end? Jesus' reply mingles together references to both events. This makes His answer difficult to understand, but conveys an important truth. Although the destruction of the Temple and the end of the world are not simultaneous events, they are nevertheless connected. The destruction of Jerusalem, including the Temple, in AD 70 was part of the process of the coming of God's Kingdom. It prefigured the coming final judgment on evil.

---

5. Read Matthew 24:30-31 again.

a. What can you learn from this passage about the nature of Jesus' second coming?

b. How do the following cross-references reinforce and expand this teaching?

Matthew 16:27

1 Thessalonians 4:16-17

Revelation 1:7

---

6. Read verses 32-51 in Matthew 24.

   a. What does this passage teach about the timing of Jesus'
   return?

   b. What do the following cross-references add?

   Matthew 25:1-13

   1 Thessalonians 5:1-11

"The truth is that the events of Jesus' incarnation, crucifixion, resurrection, ascension and second coming are in a real sense parts of *one act of God.* They are all part of the coming of God's kingly rule, and the climax is only delayed by the mercy of God who desires to give men opportunity to respond to the gospel. Therefore, in a real sense the second coming is always near, ever since Jesus began the new era through his life, death and resurrection."[2] — STEPHEN TRAVIS

ASK YOURSELF: How can an understanding of the events surrounding Christ's return help me?

For Further Study

The conflict between God (and good) and Satan (and evil) is described in various places in the Bible. This conflict reaches its climax with the return of Christ.

A. How does 2 Thessalonians 2:1-12 describe the escalation of the conflict?

B. What do you learn in 1 John 2:18-23 and 4:1-3?

C. The most complete description is found in Revelation. This is a difficult book to understand because of the imagery that is used. (*Highlights of the Book of Revelation,* by George

Beasley, is a short and helpful introduction.) Try reading chapters 5-19 of Revelation rapidly. What can you learn about

the reality and fierceness of the forces of evil?

God's ultimate triumph?

D. How should this understanding affect our attitude toward life?

An Awesome Climax
Then the end will come.
(1 Corinthians 15:24)

Christians have different views about the order of events at the end of time. These center around the question of whether the thousand-year reign of Christ pictured in Revelation 20 is literal or symbolic, and whether it occurs before or after His return. One scholar, James Orr, has written, "My own opinion is that the distinction between symbol and outward fact must remain more or less an uncertainty till the time itself shall declare it." In this section, we will consider the consequences of Christ's return without attempting to indicate a detailed timetable.

Read Matthew 13:36-43. This is one of many warnings Jesus gives about "the end of the age." We will concentrate on verses 41-43, and look up a number of cross-references.

---

7. Read verses 41 and 42.

a. Why do you think this action is necessary?

b. What can you learn from the following verses about how it is actually accomplished?

John 5:28-29

2 Thessalonians 1:8-10

Revelation 20:10-15

8. Focus on Matthew 13:43.

   a. How would you describe the future of the righteous?

   b. What can you learn about our resurrected bodies from
      1 Corinthians 15:35-57 and Philippians 3:20-21?

   c. How should this affect our attitude toward death? Also
      see 1 Thessalonians 4:13-18.

   d. What light do the following passages shed on the trans-
      formation of the present physical world into the
      Kingdom?

      Romans 8:18-25

2 Peter 3:10-13

e. According to Revelation 21:22-27, what will be the central feature of the Kingdom?

f. Why do you think the righteous will shine?

ASK YOURSELF: How can these future events become more real to me?

A Dynamic Hope

Praise be to the God and Father
of our Lord Jesus Christ!
In his great mercy
he has given us new birth into a living hope
through the resurrection of Jesus Christ
from the dead.
(1 Peter 1:3)

Most of the passages we have considered stress the practical implications of our hope in the glorious return of Jesus Christ. In this section we will concentrate on 2 Peter 3:1-14. As you complete this section, think particularly about how the assurance that Jesus Christ will return should affect our daily living.

"Walter, come down from there this minute
or that's the last book on the Second Coming I get you!"

9. Read verses 1-9.

   a. Verse 1 refers to the importance of right (wholesome) thinking. What place do you think the return of Christ should have in our thoughts?

   b. What facts can help us to maintain our hope in the midst of an unbelieving society?

10. Focus on 2 Peter 3:9.

   a. How should the knowledge of the return of Christ affect our evangelism?

   b. How does Matthew 24:14 link evangelism and the return of Christ?

c. How could this relate to the call in 2 Peter 3:12 to speed His coming?

11. Read verses 10-14 of 2 Peter 3. How do you think our knowledge of the future and hope of a new creation should cause us to live now?

> **ASK YOURSELF:** How is the hope of the return of Christ influencing my daily life?

Stop, Think, and Pray

What have you learned about Jesus' return? How has God inspired you as you have spent time considering this truth? How can you make sure that it continues to influence the way you live?

Suggested memory verses about expecting the return of Christ

For the Lord himself will come down from heaven, with a loud command, with the voice of the archangel and with the trumpet call of God, and the dead in Christ will rise first. After that, we who are still alive and are left will be caught up with them in the clouds to meet the Lord in the air. And so we will be with the Lord forever.
(1 Thessalonians 4:16-17)

NOTES: 1. Bruce Milne, *Know the Truth* (Leicester, England: InterVarsity Press, 1982), page 254.
2. Stephen Travis, *The Jesus Hope* (London: Word Books, 1974), page 53.

Developing World Vision

1. Gather facts about the state of world evangelization, and pray. *Operation World*, by Patrick Johnstone, is an invaluable resource. It combines a brief survey of every country of the world with a practical, day-by-day prayer guide.
2. Adopt missionaries. Read their letters so you can pray for them about specific needs and answered prayers. Support them financially if possible.
3. Read missionary biographies.
4. Read a book about other religions and think about the challenge of reaching the followers.
5. Be alert to those around you from other countries and of other faiths.

Memorizing Scripture

As You Start to Memorize a Verse

1. Read in your Bible the context of each verse you memorize.
2. Try to gain a clear understanding of what each verse actually means. (You may want to read the verse in other Bible translations or paraphrases to get a better grasp of the meaning.)
3. Read the verse several times thoughtfully, aloud or in a whisper. This will help you grasp the verse as a whole. Each time you read it, say the topic, reference, verse, and then the reference again.
4. Discuss the verse with God in prayer, and continue to seek His help for success in Scripture memory.

While You Are Memorizing a Verse

5. Work on saying the verse aloud as much as possible.
6. Learn the topic and reference first.
7. After learning the topic and reference, learn the first phrase of the verse. Once you have learned the topic, reference, and first phrase and have repeated them several times, continue adding more phrases, one at a time.
8. Think about how the verse applies to you and your daily circumstances.
9. Always include the topic and reference as part of the verse as you learn it and review it.

After You Have Memorized a Verse

10. Write the verse from memory and check your accuracy. This deepens the impression in your mind.
11. Review the verse immediately after learning it, and repeat it frequently in the next few days. This is crucial for getting the verse firmly fixed in your mind, because of how quickly we tend to forget what we have recently learned.
12. REVIEW! REVIEW! REVIEW! Repetition is the best way to engrave the verse on your memory.

Who's Who

Below, listed in alphabetical order, are brief biographical sketches of figures from the history of the Church who are quoted in this book.

Booth, William (1829-1912)
Pawnbroker's apprentice from Nottingham, England, who went on to found the Salvation Army and act as its first general. The movement demonstrated a concern for the poor and a crusading evangelical zeal. By the time of Booth's death, there were sixteen thousand officers in fifty-eight countries.

Crysostom, John (354-407)
Monk from Antioch who became Patriarch of Constantinople. An outstanding orator, his godliness and reforming zeal resulted in his ill-treatment, exile, and death.

King, Jr., Martin Luther (1929-1968)
Black American civil rights leader and Baptist pastor. He led non-violent demonstrations against racial discrimination and won the passage of the Civil Rights Act of 1964 and 1965. He was awarded the 1964 Nobel Peace Prize.

Lightfoot, Joseph B. (1828-1889)
Nineteenth-century Cambridge scholar whose careful historical research on the New Testament and early Christian literature

helped refute the contemporary skeptical criticism of biblical faith. He wrote a number of outstanding commentaries on the letters of Paul and became an energetic Bishop of Durham.

Martyn, Henry (1781-1812)
Missionary to India and Persia. He worked with William Carey in India in evangelism and translation work. When in need of a rest, he decided to go to Persia instead of home to England. In Persia, he preached and translated the New Testament before his death.

Spurgeon, Charles (1834-1892)
Victorian Baptist renowned for his direct and powerful preaching. Before he was 20 years old, he became the pastor of New Park Street Chapel in London and soon drew vast crowds. The six-thousand-seat Metropolitan Tabernacle was erected and Spurgeon preached there regularly for thirty years. He also founded a college for pastors and trained some nine hundred men before his death.

Tertullian (160-about 220)
A Roman lawyer, he was converted in mid-life. He lived and worked in North Africa and became the first theologian to write in Latin. He was a brilliant writer, especially in defending Christianity against opponents. Later he joined the Montanist movement.

Trotman, Dawson (1906-1956)
An American whose burden for world evangelization and vision for multiplying workers led him to found The Navigators, an international missionary organization dedicated to those ends.

Wesley, John (1703-1791)
A great preacher of the English evangelical revival. Although already a Church of England minister, he came to a living faith in 1738. Prevented from speaking in churches, he traveled some two hundred fifty thousand miles and preached some forty thousand sermons in the open air. He organized the converts into classes and societies, which developed into the Methodist Church after his death.

For Further Reading

1. Belonging to the Church of Christ
Balchin, John, *What the Bible Teaches about the Church*, Tyndale House Publishers

Gibbs, Eddie, *I Believe in Church Growth*, Eerdmans Publishing Company

Milne, Bruce, *Know the Truth*, InterVarsity Press

2. Being Witnesses for Christ
Chapman, John, *Know and Tell the Gospel*, NavPress

Green, Michael, *Evangelism in the Early Church*, Eerdmans Publishing Company

Manley-Pippert, Rebecca, *Out of the Saltshaker*, InterVarsity Press

Petersen, Jim, *Evangelism as a Lifestyle*, NavPress

Petersen, Jim, *Evangelism for Our Generation*, NavPress

Watson, David, *I Believe in Evangelism*, Eerdmans Publishing Company

3. Strengthening New Believers in Christ
Eims, LeRoy, *The Lost Art of Disciplemaking*, Zondervan Publishing House

Henrichsen, Walter, *Disciples Are Made, Not Born*, Victor Books/Scripture Press

Hull, Bill, *Jesus Christ Disciplemaker*, NavPress

Robertson, Roy, *The Timothy Principle*, NavPress

4. Evangelizing the World for Christ
Douglas, J.D., ed., *Let the Earth Hear His Voice*, World Wide
   Publications
Eims, LeRoy, *Laboring in the Harvest*, NavPress
Johnstone, Patrick, *Operation World*, STL Books
The Lion Handbook to World Religions, Lion Publishing
   Corporation

5. Changing Society with Christ
Scott, Waldron, *Bring Forth Justice*, Eerdmans Publishing
   Company
Sine, Tom, *The Mustard Seed Conspiracy*, Word, Inc.

6. Expecting the Return of Christ
Milne, Bruce, *Know the Truth*, InterVarsity Press
Travis, Stephen, *The Jesus Hope*, Word, Inc.